This fab Brownie Annual 2001 beLongs to

Essential info about me

Birthday _____

Age _____

Stick a drawing or photo of yourself here.

Most important things for me

Other people I live with are

My pet is a

and is called

Stick a drawing or photo of your pet here.

My best friend is

Stick a drawing or photo of you with your best friend here.

What I want to be is

If I was a chocolate bar I'd be a

The person I'd most like to meet is

For more fab filling-in fun turn to the end of your Annual.

Brownies is the best!

Brownies have a fun-packed time, doing masses of exciting activities. There are loads of amazing reasons to be a Brownie!

It's good to be safe

You should be able to have a go at everything in your great annuals but sometimes it's wise to ask an adult you know for help. You can still do it by yourself, just make sure the adult says it's okay and is watching you. There is a note on some pages reminding you to ask for help. If there isn't one and you're still unsure, just ask for help anyway.

Badgework

On most pages of this fab *Brownie Annual 2001* there's a badgework box. The badges show where ideas and activities on that page fit into the Brownie programme. If you want to find out what you have to do to get the badge, look it up in your *Brownie Guide Badge Book*. For most badges there are quite a few things you have to do, but the most important thing is to always do your best.

Go! is a great part of the Brownie programme. You need to be nine years old to start it, but don't let this stop you having a go at these pages!

These badges show the parts of your Brownie Guide programme that are covered on the page.

Brownies are friendly	Brownies have fun out-of-doors
Brownies keep healthy	Brownies make things
Brownies are wide awake	Brownies help at home
Brownies lend a hand	Brownies do their best

Photograph by Diane Aynac. Fred by Bill Ledger

Brownie
Annual 2001

Brownie Guide Promise

I promise that I will do my best:
To love my God,
To serve the Queen and my country,
To help other people
and
To keep the Brownie Guide Law.

Freda

Freda is always on hand to help you out and to remind you of your Brownie Guide Promise. All through your Annual she's got loads of ideas. Watch out for her!

Brownie Guide Law

A Brownie Guide thinks of others before herself and does a Good Turn everyday.

THE GUIDE ASSOCIATION
A registered charity

www.guides.org.uk

Brownie Guide Motto

Lend a Hand.

Web safe

My Brownie code for safety on the World Wide Web. I promise that:

* I will agree with my parents'/guardians' rules for me using a computer, and the World Wide Web.
* I will not give my address or my telephone number without permission.
* I will not give my school's name and address without permission.
* I will say 'No' if anyone who I've met on the World Wide Web wants to meet me, unless my parent(s)/guardian(s) have agreed and will go with me.
* I won't put my photograph on a web site.
* I will tell my parent(s)/guardian(s) or teacher if I discover something on the World Wide Web which worries or upsets me.

With thanks to the Girl Scouts of the USA for the initial ideas contained within this warning for children.

Contents

There's so much to see and do in the 2001 Brownie Annual.

8 On your bike!

Have a go at exciting off-road cycling.

10 Stripy horse?

All the facts on zebras plus a great puzzle.

12 Lookin' good, feelin' great

Get into customising your clothes.

14 Escape at bedtime

A great poem with a fun space maze.

16 Caring for cats

Find out if you have what it takes to look after a cat.

18 Digits at work

Get the facts about how a computer works.

20 Early morning energy

Yummy breakfast recipes and a great wordsearch.

22 Sisters, not twins

The story of two sisters who don't always get on.

26 Tricky moments

Magic and tricks to fool your mates with.

28 Bangladesh

Find out the facts on this 30-year-old country.

The Brownie Guides who appear in this Annual are from 38th Croydon (St Alban's Pack), 43rd Derby Pack, 2nd Pilgrim's Hatch Pack, 1st West Finchley Pack and 8th West Finchley Pack.

Special thanks to: Neil Simpson at the British Cycling Federation (On your bike!); Chris Lawrence and Amanda Bailey at the RSPCA (Caring for cats); missdorothy.com Ltd (Miss Dorothy competition); Jess Gower and Justine Pannett at The Blue Cross (Passion for pets).

Clothes Brownies' own or from The Guide Association Trading Service (for details call 0800 838 227), Next Retail (stores nationwide), New Look (for stockists call 0500 454 094) and Tammy (some items may not be available).

THE GUIDE ASSOCIATION TRADING SERVICE NEXT NEW LOOK

Stripy horse?, Caring for cats, Tricky moments, Bangladesh, Extreme south, Night in day! and Deep water compiled by John and Hilary Malam; Super Brownie goes to camp written by Marion Thompson; Lookin' good, feelin' great, New kid on the block and Hair flair! complied by Jenny Wackett.

All Brownie photographs by Diana Aynaci. All Guide photographs by Moose Azim. Freda illustrated by Bill Ledger.

2001 Brownie Annual © The Guide Association 2000

Photographs © as acknowledged in features: all other photographs © The Guide Association. 'Sisters, not twins' © 1998 Jenny Swanson appears in STORY OF THE YEAR 6 published by Scholastic Ltd, reproduced by permission of the publisher. 'Jolly blue giant' © Dick King-Smith, extracted from JUNGLE JINGLES AND OTHER ANIMAL POEMS by Dick King-Smith, published by Corgi, a division of Transworld Publishers, all rights reserved.

Published by The Guide Association (a registered charity), 17–19 Buckingham Palace Road, London, SW1W 0PT
E-mail: chq@guides.org.uk Web site: www.guides.org.uk
ISBN 0 85260 163 8
The Guide Association Trading Service ordering code: 60053

An official publication of The Guide Association (incorporated by Royal Charter) registered charity number 306016

Readers are reminded that during the life span of this publication there may be changes to The Guide Association's policy, or legal requirements, that will affect the accuracy of the information contained within these pages.

Patrons HM The Queen, HM Queen Elizabeth, The Queen Mother President HRH The Princess Margaret, Countess of Snowdon World Chief Guide (1930–1977) Olave, Lady Baden-Powell, GBE Chief Guide Bridget Towle Brownie Guide Adviser Sandra Moffitt Senior Project Editor Alice Forbes Editor Annabelle Mundy Special Project Designer David Jones Design Team Manager Gillian Webb Studio Jade Garner, Joanne Harkness, Quentin Radburn, Diana Rang, Cathy Summers, Stephen Turnham, Alexandra Valy Production Stuart Bannerman Colour repro Argent Colour Ltd Printed and bound in Italy by Officine Grafiche De Agostini.

THE GUIDE ASSOCIATION

30 Box it up
Make these fabulous boxes for your jewels and accessories.

32 Polar puzzles
Lots of fun at the frozen ends of the Earth.

34 Groovy Guides
Get the facts on Guides.

36 Fantasy feast
Some really revolting recipes.

38 New kid on the block
A photostory about making new friends also with a special puzzle.

42 Cool computer
Loads of puzzles linked to computers.

44 Extreme south
Find out about this remote and freezing part of the world.

46 Technostyle
Great things to make with unwanted CDs.

48 Miss Dorothy Competition
Your chance to win a fab computer!

50 Read all about it!
Great ideas for getting out there and telling others how great Brownies is.

52 Night in day!
The hot facts on eclipses, with a puzzle to test you.

54 Cool cooks

Freezing recipes that are yummy scrummy.

56 Jolly blue giant
A poem about whales.

58 Guides are great!
Fill-in fun and a great quiz about Guides.

60 Passion for pets
Find out what it takes to be a vet.

62 The great game!
A fun African game to make and an exciting maze.

64 Super Brownie
More exciting tales of Super Brownie at Guide camp.

68 Hair flair!
Get stuck in to grips and clips to create a new hair style for yourself.

70 Deep water
Find out what's at the ocean bottom and have fun with the maze.

72 Cook-out capers
Great recipes for barbecues and at camp.

74 Animal antics
Animal puzzles to have fun with and test your skills.

76 Get it right?
See how well you did at all the puzzles in this great Brownie Annual.

All illustrations as acknowledged on appropriate pages.

On your bike!

Got some wheels? Why not get out and about, and have some fun off-road? First off, get to grips with what it's all about.

Corners

If the ground is slippery it's important to know how to go round corners. It may surprise you that you can go round corners without turning the handlebars. Try pushing your bike from the saddle. When it is upright it goes straight. Tilt the seat to the right or left and that's the way the bike goes.

Where to go

There are loads of places you can go that's not on the road, but you shouldn't cycle on footpaths or pavements. Always slow down near people walking, especially if they have little children or dogs, and near horses. So, find yourself an open space, path or bridleway where cycling is allowed.

Left-hand bend

Don't go too fast into a corner, but going slowly actually makes it harder.

Glorious mud

Mud is great fun, but leave it where you found it. Cycling can damage ground, so you should be careful to keep to paths.

As you come up to the corner look at where you want to go. Keep pedalling.

As you go into the corner place your weight onto your right foot with your pedal at the bottom.

Right gear

Knowing the right gear to be in is important. As the going gets harder and heavier you want to start dropping to lower, easier gears. Practise changing gears until you can do it without thinking. Remember, for the chain to move cogs you need to be pedalling. The back gears are changed with your right lever.

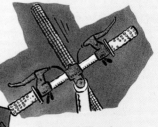

Stop pedalling for a moment. At the same time lean onto your left hand making your bike lean left.

As the bike goes to the left start pedalling again. Start to straighten up.

Now try a right-hand corner.

Braking

The right lever works the front brake and the left the rear one. The front brake stops the bike quickly, but sometimes too fast so the back of the bike comes off the ground and knocks you over the handlebars. It is usually best to use both brakes using the rear one slightly before the front. Avoid braking quickly. Try to slow down gently.

Hands ready

Have your fore and middle fingers ready over the brake levers. Hold on tight with the other fingers. Practise moving your thumb quickly to change gears.

Practise stopping

Brake when you're not going too fast. Feel how much you have to pull the levers. Try using just the front brake. Was it harder to steer? Now just the rear one. Did the wheel lock or skid a bit? It's important not to skid as this damages the ground – and you may fall off.

Uphill

On a steep hill it may be tempting to pedal standing up. If you pedal sitting down, your weight is over the back tyre keeping it firmly on the ground. This means that the energy you put into pedalling gets you up the hill, instead of skidding round.

Downhill

Stand up in your pedals keeping them both at the same level. Stretch out so some of your weight is over the back of the bike. Don't tense up and keep your shoulders, elbows and wrists relaxed. Don't forget to keep braking gently.

Masses of fun

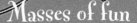

The best way to learn more off-road cycling skills is with a cycle club. Find out about one near you from the British Cycling Federation on 0161 230 2301, then press ★5. Visit www.bcf.uk.com for club information as well.

BRITISH CYCLING FEDERATION

Be safe!

Wear an approved helmet that fits. ★ Be seen. Wear light, bright clothes. ★ Keep your eyes open to what's going on round you. Remember to look behind, too. ★ Make sure your brakes and lights work well. ★ Follow the Highway Code on the road. ★ Don't carry anything but yourself on your bike. ★ Get an adult to make sure you are safe before cycling on the road.

Oxford Scientific Films/Stan Osolinski

Zebras look like stripy horses, but are they really that? Here's your chance to get all the info on these beautiful animals.

Stripy horse?

Different kinds

Zebras are related to horses, and of course are easy to spot by their black and white stripes. There are three kinds, or species, of zebra:

◆ Plains Zebra.
◆ Grevy's Zebra.
◆ Mountain Zebra.

Hiding stripes

A zebra's stripes help to hide it from its enemies. They make a zebra blend into the background so it's hard to see. This is called camouflage. Each type of zebra has its own basic pattern. Grevy's Zebra has very narrow stripes that are close together, while the stripes of the Plains and Mountain Zebras are wider.

Green food

Zebras are herbivores. This means they only eat plants, especially grass and leafy plants. When they are grazing their lips are constantly moving, feeling for plants and bending them towards their mouths. Next time you see a horse grazing take a look to see how they do this.

Life in Africa

Zebras are only found in the wild in Africa. The Plains Zebra roams African grasslands from Sudan in the north down to South Africa. Grevy's Zebra and the Mountain Zebra live mostly in the semi-desert regions of Ethiopia and Somalia.

Unique pattern

Each of the three zebras has its own stripe pattern.
Also, no two zebras have exactly the same pattern.
Just like every human has a different fingerprint,
each zebra has its own unique stripe pattern.

Growing up

When a foal is born its mother quickly licks
it clean. Within fifteen minutes it can stand
up and walk. It stays with its mother for a
year. Then it begins to live on its own. A
zebra usually lives for about 20 years.

Family Life

Zebras live in families with one
male, several females and their foals.
Families live together in herds. Living in
herds gives protection from predators as they
can look out for each other.

Predators

Lions, cheetahs and hyenas are
some of a zebra's natural enemies.
These animals hunt zebras for
food. By itself, a zebra's only
chance is to run away. It can run
up to 65 kilometres an hour but
it gets tired quickly and can't
keep going that fast for long. By
living in a herd, a predator finds
it harder to pick out one zebra to
kill. Also a predator knows it is in
danger of being trampled.

Hunting

Humans are an enemy too, as
hunters kill zebras for their skins.
Both the Grevy's Zebra and the
Mountain Zebra are endangered
species, which means
that they are in danger
of dying out.

No neigh

Unlike horses, zebras do not
neigh. Instead, they make
barking and squealing noises.

Tell them apart

Spot six differences between these two zebras.

Check out how well you
did on page 76.

11

Lookin' good,

Fancy a clear-out of your wardrobe? Got the cash to get totally trendy? Well here's the easiest way to be completely cool, without breaking the bank.

Sizzling summer shoes

You need
old trainers that fit you ★ ruler ★ fabric paint and brush ★ strong fabric ★ scissors ★ iron and board ★ braid or ribbon ★ needle and thread ★ iron-on hemming fabric ★ glue ★ velcro strip ★ insoles (optional)

Top tips
Ask an adult for help. ★ Cover your work area with old newspaper before you start.

Measure your trainers like this. Remove the laces. Paint the trainers all over. Let them dry.

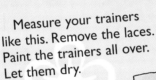

2 Cut some fabric twice as wide and 5cm longer than the measurements you took.

3 Iron a 2½cm hem at each end. Iron the piece in half. Secure with a strip of iron-on hemming fabric.

4 Sew a piece of braid to one end. Attach the velcro patch to the reverse of the fabric and to the outside edge of the trainer.

5 Pull the fabric into place. Check it fits, then glue the other end in place. Add insoles for extra comfort!

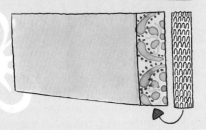

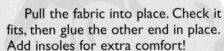

Glue

Illustrations by Stephanie Strickland

feelin' great!

Trim trousers

You need

pair of old jeans ✿ some loud fabric ✿ scissors ✿ iron and board ✿ pins ✿ needle and thread ✿ tape measure

1 Measure the distance round the waistband and its depth. Double the depth and add 5cm on both dimensions.

2 Cut a piece of fabric using these dimensions. Iron the ends of the fabric over as shown.

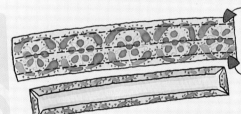

2½cm

3 Pin and sew the fabric just below the outside edge. Pin and sew on the inside. Then sew the ends.

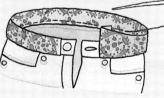

5 Cut the fabric and iron the ends as in step 2. Mark the middle and pin in place at the bottom of the outside seam.

2½ cm

6 Pin round the bottom. Sew into place. Pin round the top. Make little tucks if needed to make it fit. Sew round then down the outside seam.

Cool t-shirt

You need

plain colour t-shirt ✿ fabric pens ✿ sequins ✿ needle and cotton

Design your own trendy label. Draw it onto your t-shirt. Colour it with the fabric pens. Then brighten it up by sewing on sequins.

4 Measure round the bottom of the leg. Decide how deep you want your strip, then add 5cm on both dimensions.

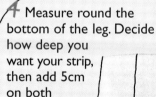

Take a look at the great hair ideas on page 68.

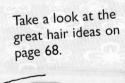

Dream up your own designer label!

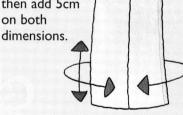

13

Escape at bedtime

The lights from the parlour and kitchen shone out
  Through the blinds and the windows and bars;
And high overhead and all moving about,
  There were thousands of millions of stars.
There ne'er were such thousands of leaves on a tree,
  Nor of people in church or the Park,
As the crowds of the stars that looked down upon me,
  And that glittered and winked in the dark.

The Dog, and the Plough, and the Hunter, and all,
  And the star of the sailor, and Mars,
These shone in the sky, and the pail by the wall
  Would be half full of water and stars.
They saw me at last, and they chased me with cries,
  And they soon had me packed into bed;
But the glory kept shining and bright in my eyes,
  And the stars going round in my head.

Robert Louis Stevenson

Asteroids

Dodge the flying asteroids to
get home safely.

How good an astronaut are you?

Check out page 76.

Illustrations by David Pattison and Tom Clayton

Caring for cats

A pet cat can be fantastic fun, but it's really important to be able to look after it properly. Make sure you've got the know-how by following these great tips from the RSPCA.

Want a kitten?

A kitten must be at least eight weeks old before it is ready to leave its mother. You need to house train it, and be prepared for it to damage furniture. Kittens like to play a lot and need lots of attention. All kittens need vaccinations and should be neutered as soon as possible. Ask your vet for advice.

Oxford Scientific Films/E.R. Degginger

Food

You don't have to use cat foods from tins and packets but they do contain all the correct proteins, minerals and vitamins that your cat needs. How much to give your cat is printed on the packaging. Kittens need five small meals a day. By six months old they only need to be fed twice a day.

Think of a cat

Cats are more independent and are usually house trained. Animal shelters tend to have lots of rescued cats to choose from if you can prove you will offer it a good home.

What to look for

Look for a kitten or cat with shiny, healthy fur that isn't skinny or has a bulging tummy. Don't pick one with runny eyes or sneezing nose, or one with a cough. Make sure round its bottom is clean and dry. Check its ears are clean and avoid one with fleas.

Grass and water

Kittens and cats needs lots of fresh water. Keep the food and water bowls clean. Cats need to eat grass so make sure your cat gets outside regularly, or put some fresh grass in a pot by the water bowl.

Sleep anywhere!

Kittens and cats need a dry, warm, clean and comfortable bed. It doesn't have to be expensive and a deep cardboard box lined with newspaper can be very cosy. If your cat doesn't like it it'll find somewhere better to sleep – maybe your bed!

Oxford Scientific Films/Alan & Sandy Carey

Toilet training

You may need to train your pet to use a litter tray. Plastic trays are good as they don't leak. Fill it with sand or dry soil, or you can buy cat litter. Empty it every day, and clean it well with hot soapy water.

Out and about

A cat must be able to get in and out of the house when it wants, so you may need to fit a cat-flap. Cats without this freedom tend to go missing, find a new home or get into lots of fights.

Grooming

Short-haired cats only need to be brushed when they are moulting. Long-haired kittens and cats should be combed then brushed every day.

Holiday time

If you go on holiday you must arrange for your cat to be looked after by someone who lives nearby or for it to stay at a cattery. It is possible to take pets abroad, but there are strict rules.

Get it right

Go through these questions with an adult you live with.

Can you afford £120 for vaccinations and neutering?

Will your family mind if it damages furniture?

Will you have £5 a week for food?

Is there somewhere outside a cat can play safely?

Are you willing to empty the litter tray every day?

Can someone look after your cat when you're away, or can you afford a cattery?

If you answer yes to every one, then a cat may be a good pet for you.

More info

There are lots more things you need to know before getting a kitten or cat. A special booklet called *Cats and kittens* is available from the RSPCA, Causeway, Horsham, West Sussex RH12 1HG, e-mail enquiries@rspca.org.uk or phone 01403 264181.

RSPCA

Take a look at the RSPCA web site www.rspca.org.uk as well.

Computers only know two numbers, zero and one. Find out here how such complex machines use such a simple system.

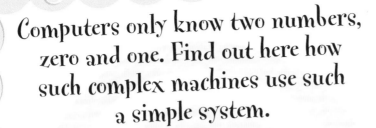

Digits

Binary system

We count on a decimal system of one to ten. Computers use a binary system where zero and one make sense of our decimal numbers.

Bits

The zeros and ones are called bits, which is short for binary digits. Having a choice of only zero or one is like having a light switch off or on. The bits work in the computer to turn a tiny electrical charge off or on.

Keyboard connection

The computer doesn't know the keys on the keyboard as letters and symbols. Each key is coded with a number (in binary, of course). When you tap a key, a series of electrical pulses tells the computer which one it is.

Mouse moves

Inside a most mice are two small wheels that the mouse ball turns. These turn off and on two lights. From the light pulses the computer can work out a binary number for each wheel. Using both numbers together it can work out where the mouse is. The computer sees the screen as a grid of numbers so it knows where to put the arrow (or cursor). It's a bit like a map reference.

As the mouse moves the numbers change and tell the computer where to move the pointer on screen.

Screen hotspots

An icon on the screen is a hotspot. The computer understands that a certain area means something special like the wastebin or a programme. When the reference from the mouse matches the ones on screen the computer knows to activate it when you click.

Illustrations by John Haslam Computer photographs courtesy of Apple Computer

Programs

A computer program is a complicated series of commands that tell the computer what to do. A computer programmer translates instructions that you may want your computer to do using a language your computer can understand. Your computer needs enough memory to store them and run them.

Memory space

Remember every zero or one is called a bit. Eight zeros and ones together (eight bits) are called a byte. Roughly, pressing one key takes one byte of memory.

        1 byte = 1 letter
   1 kilobyte (1Kb) = 1,024 bytes – about a paragraph (150 words)
 1 megabyte (1Mb) = 1,048,576 bytes – about a novel, or a floppy disk
   1 gigabyte (1Gb) = 1,073,741,824 bytes

A CD holds about 650Mb, but pictures and sound take up a lot of memory.

ROM and RAM

Your computer uses its memory very carefully to run programs and remember information. The read-only memory (ROM) remembers instructions that are never changed, like how to start up when it is switched on. The random access memory (RAM) remembers only current information for as long as it needs.

Think about how you remember things during the day...

7.30am	**clean teeth**	**must remember then** forget **until bedtime**
7.45am	**take lunch and homework**	**must remember**
8.00am	**meet friends**	**must remember what was on telly last night, then okay to** forget
9.00am	**hand in homework**	**okay to** forget **now**
10.30am	**break time**	**remember rules of the game for 15 minutes**
10.45am	**reading**	**remember how to read, remember what was happening in the story**
12.30pm	**eat lunch**	**okay to** forget **about food until later**

...and so on.

Like you, your computer knows what it needs to remember for a long time, or what it can remember for a short while before it is okay to forget.

They even draw me on a computer!

EarLy MorNING energy

Top tips
Ask an adult to help you in the kitchen. ✿ Always wash your hands before cooking. ✿ Tie back long hair.

Have an eggs-tra special start to your day and cram yourself full of energy with these tasty breakfast feasts.

Eggy bread

Ingredients
2 eggs ★ 50ml milk ★ salt and pepper ★ 2 slices bread ★ a little butter

You need
bowl ★ fork ★ frying pan ★ fish slice

Mix the eggs, milk, salt and pepper. Dip the bread into the mixture and cover both sides. Heat the butter in the frying pan. Place the bread in the pan. When one side is cooked, turn it over and cook the other side.

Crunchy munchies

Ingredients
⅓ cup small porridge oats ✿ raisins or sultanas ✿ pumpkin seeds ✿ sunflower seeds ✿ almonds or other nuts ✿ banana chips ✿ chocolate drops ✿ honey or sugar ✿ milk or orange juice to serve

You need
bowl ✿ spoon

Put the oats in a bowl. Add as much or as little of the other ingredients as you want. Remember, it's easier to add more, but taking away from the mixture is hard. Make sure your combination is nice and crunchy! Add a little sugar or honey just before serving with milk or orange juice.

Illustrations by Bill Ledger

Cook's know-how
Make it again using different amounts of each ingredient, or try something exotic like papaya or mango pieces.

Sunrise surprise

Ingredients
pineapple chunks
grapefruit segments
satsuma or tangerine
segments
cranberry juice
yoghurt or fromage
frais ✿ cherries

You need
can opener ✿ bowl
(a glass one looks good!)
✿ spoon

Put some pineapple chunks with grapefruit and satsuma segments in a bowl. Poor over some cranberry juice. Add two scoops of yoghurt. Place some cherries on the top.

On the plate

A glass of cold milk, or some fresh orange juice, makes your breakfast even yummier.

Breakfast brains

Find all these breakfast and early morning words in the word square below.

dew	cream	muffin	breakfast
tea	frost	morning	dawn chorus
milk	toast	sausage	orange juice
mist	banana	sunrise	hot chocolate
alarm	cereal	yoghurt	scrambled egg
bacon	coffee	porridge	

```
D A W N C H O R U S O G
E O O B R A E T S O R F
W D M R E E F F O C A M
O R O E A M U F F I N G
S C R A M B L E D E G G
A E N K I A L A R M E A
U R I F S C M I L K J N
S E N A T O A S T I U A
A A G S U N R I S E I N
G L N T R U H G O Y C A
E G E G D I R R O P E B
E T A L O C O H C T O H
```

Starting in the top left corner, put the left-over letters in the boxes below. What's the special message?

☐ ☐ ☐ ☐ ☐ ☐ ☐ ☐ ☐ ☐ ☐ ☐

Check out your answers on page 76.   21

Sisters,

It isn't easy being a sister. Laurie and Lulu did not agree often, but they did agree on that. And it certainly isn't easy being sisters, if you look like twins when you're not. Laurie and Lulu had been born two years apart, but Laurie was small for her age, while Lulu was tall for hers. So they were just about the same size. Unluckily they also looked very alike, with long straight hair. Laurie's eyebrows were a little crooked, and Lulu's mouth was slightly wider, but you wouldn't notice unless you looked hard at them both. Which nobody ever did.

Because they were alike on the outside, people thought they must be alike on the inside. And they weren't. It caused all kinds of trouble. Some people also thought they should dress alike, and sent presents of identical clothes. Lulu didn't mind – she loved dressing like Laurie. But Laurie – well, she always wanted to look different.

Mum said shopping was a nightmare. When she took them to choose clothes, Lulu would never pick anything out. She waited to see what Laurie wanted, then said, "I'd like the same."

"If she's having that, I want something different," Laurie would say.

"So do I, then."

"You're a copycat! Copycat, copycat!"

Laurie would stick her tongue out and Lulu would cry. Often they would come home with nothing. Mum tried shopping alone, but if she chose clothes the same, Laurie sulked, and if she chose different ones, Lulu sulked. There was just no pleasing them both.

When Mum told the girls that they were to be bridesmaids, Lulu yelled, "Cool!"

But Laurie asked "What'll we wear?"

Mum looked at them sternly. "You'll be dressed EXACTLY alike. Bridesmaids always are."

Laurie and Lulu knew that voice – it meant NO ARGUING OR ELSE. So they didn't even ask what the clothes would be like, just carried on eating. Lulu, crunching marmite toast, imagined something pink, with a long, full skirt, stiff petticoats, and a huge bow at the back. Laurie, nibbling cocopops, saw something short, sleek, perhaps lime green? Something which would miraculously make her look at least two years older than Lulu – and preferably three.

It was not to be. When the dresses came, they fitted perfectly and Laurie had to agree that they were lovely. There was just one problem: she did look EXACTLY like Lulu.

Lulu was deliriously happy: she looked so much like Laurie, that she even felt like Laurie. And secretly she had always wanted to BE Laurie. She thought that it just wasn't fair. She was sure she would have been a far better big sister – kinder, for a start. Laurie played with her quite nicely if no one else was there, but as soon as anyone else came along, everything changed.

not twins

The week before the wedding, Laurie invited a schoolfriend for tea. Victoria made up wonderful games in the playground, and Laurie really hoped they might be best friends.

"We're going upstairs," she shouted, as soon as they came in. "Don't let Lulu bother us, Mum."

Lulu sighed. She might as well be invisible when Laurie's friends were around.

But Victoria was different. She looked right at Lulu, not through her.

"Oh Laurie, let her come and play – it's more fun with three."

"YE-E-ES!" yelled Lulu, racing up the stairs before Victoria could change her mind.

"What shall we play?" she asked.

"Dressing up?" suggested Laurie.

"Boring," said Victoria. "Let's play witches."

Laurie wanted to say that that was dressing up, too, but Victoria was bigger than her, and she really, really wanted to be best friends.

"Okay," she said. "Lulu can be the witch and chase us."

"No," grumbled Lulu. "Let's all be witches."

"I know," squealed Victoria, "let's all be children. We can imagine the witch – she lives under your stairs. She's guarding a treasure of... of... of magic pinecones." She took some from Laurie's windowsill. "Hide these in the understairs cupboard, Lulu. We'll pretend that in here we're safe, but outside is all scarymagical. We'll take turns to go on secret missions to steal the pinecones."

It was the most thrilling game that Laurie and Lulu had ever played. They closed all the curtains to make it more frightening. The landing and the stairs were Scaryland, Mum's bedroom was Skeletonland, the bathroom was Witchyland and the downstairs was Ghostyland. You had to be brave enough to visit each land in turn, before you could creep downstairs and sneak into the dark cupboard, to rescue a magic pinecone from the Wicked Witch.

At first they fetched one every time. But then Laurie heard bones rattling in Skeletonland, and Victoria heard goblins whispering in Witchyland. Mum was outside, and Ghostyland seemed lonely, and full of strange rustlings. They decided that they would only go downstairs in pairs, but even then it was creepy.

"I've had enough of this," said Laurie. "It's too scary."

"It's not!" cried Lulu.

"Come on," said Victoria, "don't be a scaredy-cat. All we need is some magic to protect us. Good magic."

"Like what?" asked Laurie suspiciously.

"Like the opposite of witches. Witches like black, and ugly things. So fairy magic should be white, and pretty sparkly things."

"We've got loads of sequins and bits of foil in the collage box," said Lulu eagerly. "If we scattered them on the ground, that might keep the goblins away."

Soon the carpets and stairs were sprinkled with little pieces of bright stuff. It did work, a little, but

goblins still whispered in the bathroom, and now crocodiles snapped on the stairs.

"Now we'll dress up," decided Victoria. "Have you got any fairy dresses?"

"Laurie's got a frilly petticoat and a sparkly hairband."

"I'll have those," said Victoria.

Laurie looked at her, then fetched them out of the wardrobe. Victoria wriggled into the petticoat, adjusted the hairband and beamed.

"That feels much safer. What about you?"

"We haven't got anything else like that," said Lulu sadly.

"I don't much want to play," said Laurie. "I'll just stay here and guard the cottage."

"I want to play," insisted Lulu. "Come and look in my room."

They tiptoed across Scaryland and crept into Lulu's room. The wardrobe door creaked and Lulu screamed. Victoria peered into the wardrobe, then brought out a cream satin frock.

"This would be great."

Lulu was shocked.

"That's my bridesmaid's outfit. I can't wear that!"

"We'd only be in the house," tempted Victoria. "I'll wear it if you're scared."

"No – it's okay," said Lulu quickly. She remembered how marvellous it had felt when she'd tried it on. Surely that would protect her from the goblins.

She squirmed into the dress and tiptoed on to the landing. It worked. There were no scary rustlings at all.

"Now we need something for the crocodiles," said Victoria. "Something sweet, so they won't feel so hungry for us."

"Mum's got hundreds and thousands. Would those do?"

"Perfect. Run and fetch them, Lulu."

Lulu crept downstairs, her heart racing. She was careful to tread on the patches of carpet where the glittering papers lay thickest. Surely the magic

would be strongest there. She dashed past the understairs cupboard and into the kitchen, snatched the hundreds and thousands from their shelf and rushed back. Laurie gave a shriek of horror.

"Lulu! Take that dress off this minute. And who said you could have the hundreds and thousands?"

"It's my dress," said Lulu sulkily, "so I can wear it if I like. Victoria said it was the right thing. And we're only going to borrow the hundreds and thousands, not eat them."

"Actually, I think we should eat a few," said Victoria. "Just to give us strength."

So they poured some into three dolls' saucers and licked it up. They did feel braver, so they refilled the saucers and left them for the crocodiles. Some spilled on the carpet, but Victoria said that was even better, and suddenly she took the lid off the container and scattered the rest of the hundreds and thousands over the top banister. They fell like rainbow drizzle upon the dark stair carpet. Laurie felt a lurch of excitement. The house didn't feel like their own dull, safe house any more. It was a truly magical land.

"I bet we could get to the bottom of the stairs in complete safety now," she said.

They tried it, and they could. Lulu laughed with joy.

"Good," chuckled Victoria. "Witches hate laughter."

"I know," squealed Lulu, "let's get rid of the witch altogether. Let's drive her out with a magic potion."

"Yes! If we all drink it at once, the witch will disintegrate," cried Victoria.

"There's Ribena in the kitchen," suggested Lulu. "Or milk?"

"I know!" cried Laurie. "Ribena IN milk. Like a magic milkshake. I'll get it."

She fetched three glasses, putting a large dollop of Ribena in each one and milk on top. It went a rich, dark blue, unlike any drink she'd seen before. She dipped a finger in and licked it. Plum! That proved it was magic – everyone knows that you can't make plums by mixing blackcurrants with milk.

They carried their drinks into the hall, then stood in a ring outside the cupboard door and raised their glasses.

"We must all drink at exactly the same moment," whispered Victoria. "If we get it wrong, the magic won't be strong enough. The witch will burst out of the cupboard and capture us. I'll count to three."

The others stood quietly, waiting. Lulu was so nervous that she felt sick. It seemed ages before Victoria began to count.

"One … two … three … DRINK."

At exactly that moment there was a loud crash. The back door slammed and Mum came into the house. They all dropped their glasses. Laurie's and Victoria's fell on the floor, but Lulu's tipped straight down the front of her bridesmaid's frock. The dark blue stain spread across the cream satin.

Mum looked at them. She looked at the mess of blue milk and broken glass on the floor. Her mouth opened and closed, but no sound came out. It looked really weird and Lulu wanted to giggle. But she knew that she mustn't, mustn't, MUSTN'T, so she pinched herself hard to keep quiet. Laurie could hear herself taking deep breaths, but she didn't feel that she was getting any air.

Mum edged past them and looked at the stairs. At the torn paper scraps, the foil, the sequins and the hundreds and thousands smeared into the carpet. She looked back at the girls.

"I think I'll go home now," squeaked Victoria, and she did. She leapt past the broken glass, opened the front door and scuttled away, even though she was only wearing a petticoat and no shoes, and had not had her tea. Lulu supposed it was lucky that she only lived round the corner.

Finally Mum got her voice back.

"Lulu Cameron," she groaned, "that frock is ruined. You won't be able to be a bridesmaid. Laurie will have to do it on her own, unless I stay angry until next week – in which case neither of you will even be at the wedding."

Lulu burst into tears, but Laurie surprised herself. Her mouth opened and words seemed to rush out by themselves.

"We didn't mean any harm! You'll have to let us go to the wedding, or Aunt Clare won't have any bridesmaids. And I won't do it on my own. If Lulu can't, I won't. We're sisters, and we ought to be bridesmaids together. Can't you wash the dress? Please?"

"I suppose I shall have to try."

Laurie and Lulu had to have a bath, although it was not nearly bath time. Then they had to go to bed, although it was not nearly bedtime either. They lay quietly, listening to the scrubbing and muttering noises as Mum tried to sort out the mess. Luckily the carpet did clean up in the end. Unluckily, the dress did not.

Supper in bed should have been a great treat, but Lulu and Laurie sat in their separate beds, thinking that food had never tasted so dull and lumpy. Then they heard Grandma Laura's voice from the downstairs hall.

"Leave it to me," she said. "I'll take both dresses away with me, and I'll ring Clare. I have a plan."

Then the girls were able to settle down to sleep, because Grandma Laura had taken charge, and they knew that her plans usually worked out. Maybe they could still both be bridesmaids after all.

On the day of the wedding, Aunt Clare did have two bridesmaids walking behind her. They were very similar to look at, and their dresses were the same style, but different colours. One was cream, but the other had been dyed forget-me-not blue, and each had a sash of the opposite shade. Grandma had wired artificial forget-me-nots among the cream roses on both head-dresses, and both bridesmaids carried posies tied with blue satin ribbons. The hairdresser had trimmed the girls' hair, and it hung smoothly beneath the cream roses: waist-length on Lulu, but now only shoulder-length on Laurie. The haircut completely changed the shape of her face. She looked at least two years older than Lulu – maybe even three. A sister, but definitely not a twin.

At the wedding reception, the groom offered to make them a Ribena milkshake each, and all the grown-ups laughed when Lulu hid under the table. But it was a long time before either girl touched hundreds and thousands again.

Jenny Swanson

'Sisters, not twins' © 1998 Jenny Swanson appears in STORY OF THE YEAR 6 published by Scholastic Ltd. Reproduced by permission of the publisher.

Illustrations by Jan Fearnley

Tricky moments

Stun your friends with these deceptively easy tricks. Can they see how it's done? Practise till you're perfect!

Tell the future

You need

writing paper ★ pen ★ envelope

1 Take the current year and times it by two. Seal this number in an envelope.

2 Ask your friend to write down the year she was born.

3 Under that date ask her to write any year from the last 10 years.

4 Ask her to write down how many years have passed between that year and this year.

5 Now ask her to write down how old she'll be on her birthday this year.

6 Ask her to add up the four numbers.

Open your envelope and show her the number you have written on it. It is the same number as the one your friend has just written!

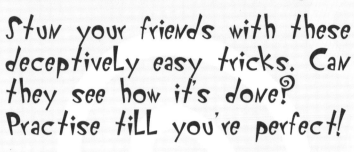

$2001 \times 2 = 4002$

1993

1997

$2001 - 1997 = 4$

8

$= 4002$

Mind reader

You need

small piece of paper ☆ pencil ☆ pack of cards

1 Before going in front of your audience, write 'It's the 8 of Hearts' on the piece of paper. Fold it up and hide it in your shoe. Then find the eight of Hearts and put it face down on the top of the pack.

2 Hold the pack behind your back. Slip the top card either into the palm of your other hand, or into your back pocket.

3 Pass the rest of the pack to your friend and ask her to shuffle the cards. Put the cards behind your back again and slip the 8 of Hearts back onto the top.

4 Give the pack back to your friend and ask her to look at the top card and remember it. Get her to put it back into the pack anywhere she likes.

5 Look through the pack and pull out any card. Put it face down near your feet so no one can see it. Ask your friend to turn it over.

6 Of course she'll say it isn't the right card. So take off your shoe and ask her to remove the paper and read your message aloud!

Cutting problem

Cut a piece of string in half then join it together without a knot in sight!

You need
two pieces of string, one 1m and the other 15cm
⭐ scissors ⭐ sticky tape
⭐ small bag of glitter

1 Before you start, make a loop from the small piece of string by joining the ends together with sticky tape. Thread the long piece through the loop.

2 Put the glitter bag in your pocket. To begin the trick, hold the strings so that your fingers hide the sticky tape and the place where the two pieces of string interlink.

3 Take the scissors and cut the small loop of string.

4 Tie the loose ends of the small loop tightly, keeping the loop hidden. Show your friends the long piece.

5 Wind the string from one end round one hand. When you get to the knot, pull it along keeping it hidden and slip it off the end.

Top tip
Practise in front of a mirror to make sure you can't see how the trick is done.

6 Pop it in your pocket and at the same time remove a handful of glitter. Sprinkle the glitter over your hand and begin to unwind the string.

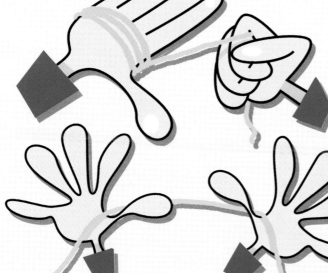

7 Unwind the long piece of string to reveal it has no knot.

Try the circus skills badge!

Illustrations by Bill Ledger

27

Bangladesh

Bangladesh is a beautiful country full of amazing creatures and plants in Asia. It was once part of India, but in 1971, 30 years ago, it became Bangladesh.

The land

Bangladesh is about half the size of Britain and most of the country is very flat. It lies at the end of three huge rivers that start high in the mountains in the north. As they flow down to the sea, the rivers travel through the flat land where they split and make new routes. This is called a river delta. Most of the people of Bangladesh live in the delta area.

Rivers

The three rivers in Bangladesh are the Ganges, the Jamuna and the Meghna. The water, as it travels down from the mountains, picks up minerals and earth called sediment. The three rivers have low banks and every year, after heavy rain, they flood the land.

Rice harvesting

Oxford Scientific Films/Paul McCullagh

Farming

Rice grows well in watery fields. It is Bangladesh's main food crop and is grown during the monsoon season. On more hilly ground, where the land is dry, tea is grown. So is jute which is used to make textiles. Along the coast fishermen catch fish to sell in local markets.

Rice

Oxford Scientific Films/Paul M

At a glance

Capital Dhaka
Population 110 million
Main religion Islam (Muslim)
Currency Taka
National day March 26

Brownies

This is what Brownies in Bangladesh look like. They meet together in large groups of about 80 and are called Yellowbirds, aged six to ten years old.

Lynnie Hutchison

Floods

These floods are usually good because the rivers leave their sediment on the land. The sediment is rich in nutrients that make the land good for farming. However, some years the floods are too much. Villages are washed away and have to be rebuilt when the water goes down.

Ganges River delta, Bangladesh

Oxford Scientific Films/NASA

Yellowbird Promise

I promise to do my best:
1 To do my duty to God and my country.
2 To help other people every day especially those at home.

Yellowbird Law

1 The Yellowbird gives in to the older folk.
2 The Yellowbird does not give in to herself.

The people

Nine out of ten people in Bangladesh are poor. Many cannot read or write, and many children do not go to school. Some children work in factories to earn money for their families. In the cities the poor often don't have fresh water or electricity.

Climate

There are three seasons in Bangladesh. From November to February the winter is cool. The dry season, from March to May, is hot and there isn't much rain. From May to October is the rainy or monsoon season when the heavy rain makes the rivers flood.

Crighton Thomas Creative

Box it up

Have you got pots of fab jewellery but nowhere special to keep it safe? Get stuck into these easy-peasy ideas and put together a collection that'll make you proud!

Curvy clay

You need
air-drying clay (from an art or craft shop) ❀ little bowl of water ❀ ruler ❀ paint and brush ❀ pva glue (optional)

Top tips
Cover your work area with a piece of old clean plastic before you start. ☆ Reseal your clay bag.

1 Take a ball of clay and roll it into a sausage a little less than 1cm thick. From one end turn it into a spiral. You may need a little water to make it stick.

2 Make another similar sausage shape. Use this to make the spiral bigger. Use water to join the ends if you need to.

3 Keep making the spiral larger until it's about 12cm in diameter. Smooth the end.

4 Lie the next sausage on top of the last one. Start building up the wall.

5 Keep going until it's about 6cm high. Smooth the end. Make a lid by repeating steps 1 to 3. Add a little ball as a handle. Leave both bits overnight to dry.

6 Mix the paint with some pva glue. Paint inside and out. Don't forget the lid. Let it dry.

Crafty know-how
Make a collection! Do different sizes. Smooth the ridges. Pick different colours for inside and out. Decorate with dazzling designs.

Illustrations by Nick Diggory

String along

You need
small box with lid ☆ string ☆ scissors ☆ glue
☆ old lollypop stick ☆ paintbrush ☆ paints

1 Cut a piece of string about 50cm long. Put a dab of glue at one end. Stick it to the corner of the box.

2 Dab more glue along the bottom of the box. Stick the string in place. Keep going till you've run out of that piece of string.

3 Cut another piece of string. Glue it in place round the box. Keep going till you reach the top.

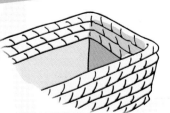

4 Work over the top edge and about 1cm down the inside. Let it dry. Turn it over and cover the bottom.

5 Paint inside the box. Then paint the string another colour. While it is drying cover the lid with string and paint it.

Stringy ideas

Use different sizes of box.
❀ Try dying the string before sticking it on.
❀ Paint a stripy pattern, using the string to guide you. ❀ Add felt flowers, stars and hearts to the outside.

Top tip
Emulsion paint used to paint walls works really well, but ask an adult for help.

Polar puzzles

Seal feeding

Find a route for the hungry seal to reach the fish.

Pick the piece
Which piece of the puzzle finishes the picture?

Cold links

Link the letters to make the words in the list. Each letter is only used once.

ice	floes	icicle	Amundsen
cold	Scott	iceberg	blue whale
flag	freeze	penguin	South Pole
snow	frozen	subzero	Antarctica

A	M	W	H	A	L	E	T	N	A
I	U	E	U	L	C	R	A	F	R
C	N	D	S	B	T	I	O	R	E
I	E	F	E	O	S	C	A	E	E
C	L	R	N	U	S	U	B	Z	Z
L	F	O	Z	T	H	L	E	P	E
O	L	F	E	N	P	O	N	E	S
E	A	E	C	I	I	U	G	C	C
S	G	W	R	G	N	I	L	O	O
S	N	O	E	B	E	C	D	T	T

Illustrations by Phil Dobson

Survival rations

Get to the Pole picking up as many supplies as you can, and missing the hazards.

Polar shadows

Match the polar bears with their shadows.

Fishing penguin

Which penguin is going to catch the fish?

Flake out

Spot the two identical flakes.

Check out your answers on page 76.

33

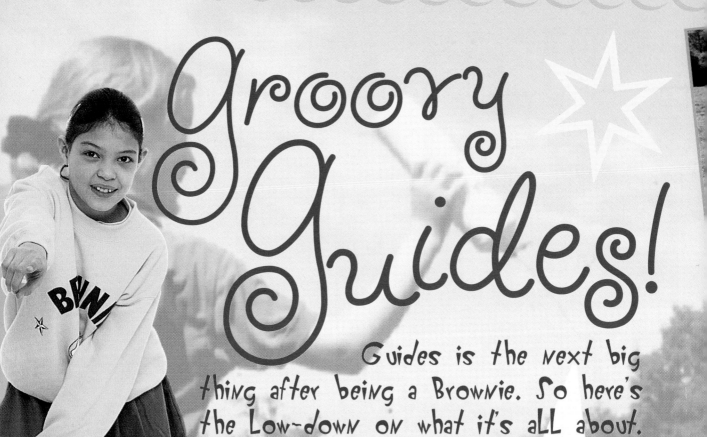

Groovy Guides!

Guides is the next big thing after being a Brownie. So here's the Low-down on what it's aLL about. Check it out and get ready to go!

Go visiting

You need to reach your tenth birthday before you can be a Guide, but don't let that stop you getting down to your local Guides to find out all about it before then. They are always having serious fun, so why not get an invite to join them?

Guide Promise

I promise that I will do my best:
To love my God,
To serve the Queen and my country,
To help other people
and
To keep the Guide Law.

Best mates

Not to worry if you don't know a Guide. When you start you'll join a Patrol which is a bit like a Six. Every Patrol parties in its own way, but before you know it you'll have the best friends you could want. Everyone gets a say in what you do, and everyone has a laugh.

Have chocolate games and get to eat it all!

Camps and holidays

Guides have a great time each year at camp or on holiday, and may even go to another country. Sometimes all the Guides go for a whole week, or for one or two weekends.

Cool things

What's so great about Guides then? Well, for a start it's up to them to choose what they want to do. They've got Guiders who help them out, but a lot of the time Guides just get on and do it! Take a look at these Guides.

Did you know?

Guides meet together in a unit. ✱ A group of four to eight Guides is called a Patrol. ✱ Guides have a Promise like the Brownie one. ✱ There are six parts to the Guide Law. ✱ Guides get to choose what to wear from a fab range of clothes.

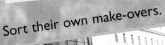

Sort their own make-overs.

Chat with their pals.

Challenges

Don't worry, there are loads of challenges to get stuck into with your Patrol, plus some badges you can try. You'll get your very own *G file* which is crammed with info on what you can get up to.

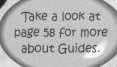

Take a look at page 58 for more about Guides.

35

Fantasy feast

Do you believe in ghosts at midnight? Cook up this ghoulish feast, then wait to see what turns up to share it with you!

Ghoul's drool

Ingredients

$^1/_2$ lemon ☆ 2 ripe avocados ☆
1 tomato ☆ salt and pepper

You need

jug ☆ chopping board ☆ knife ☆
lemon squeezer ☆ tablespoon
☆ teaspoon ☆ bowl ☆ fork

Top tips

Ask an adult to help you in the kitchen. ☆ Always wash your hands before cooking. ☆ Tie back long hair.

1 Put the tomato in the jug and cover with boiling water.

2 Cut the lemon in half. Squeeze the juice from one half.

3 Spoon the tomato out, after pouring some water from the jug. Let it cool.

4 Peel the tomato and chop it up. Add it to the bowl with the lemon juice and some salt and pepper.

5 Carefully cut the avocados in half. Remove the stone and scoop the flesh into the bowl. Mash it with the fork.

6 Dip into it with some chunky crisps or toasted bones (bread cut into bone shapes then toasted).

Scary pizza faces

Ingredients

oil ☆ 1 ready-made pizza base ☆ 1 jar tomato pizza topping ☆ cheese ☆ mushrooms ☆ green and yellow pepper ☆ sweetcorn ☆ pepperoni slices ☆ gerkhin ☆ olives ☆ ham ☆ 2 eggs

You need

baking tray ☆ spoon ☆ cheese grater ☆ knife and chopping board

Rub a little oil on the baking tray. Smooth a layer of tomato topping on top of the pizza base. Decorate the pizza in one of these ghastly ways, or make up your own horrifying features!

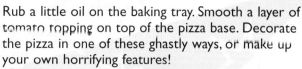

Remove the stalks from two mushrooms for the eyes. Use two slices for the eyebrows. Make the nose and lips from slices of yellow pepper. Add sweetcorn for the teeth. Give it a scary edge with cheese triangles and cheesy spots.

Make hair from ham strips. Add a green pepper mouth. Add an olive for the nose. Carefully position two raw eggs for eyes.

Sprinkle on grated cheese hair. Use pepperoni slices and olives for the eyes. Edge them with sweetcorn. Add a gerkhin slice for the mouth and an olive nose.

Cook's know-how

Check the pizza base packet for cooking instructions as some brands need to be pre-cooked before adding the tomato. Bake it in the oven for about 20–30 minutes. Pop it under the grill for a couple of minutes to sizzle the top.

Bogey slurp

Ingredients

3 scoops vanilla ice-cream ☆ banana ☆ ½ pint milk ☆ red, green and orange jelly sweets ☆ chocolate sticks

You need

foodmixer, or a bowl and whisk ☆ two glasses

Zap the ice-cream, banana and milk in the foodmixer for about a minute. Then add the sweets and mix for a couple of seconds. Pour into the glasses. Add a chocolate stick. For an extra-gooey slurpy drink use banana ice-cream instead.

On the plate

Serve at a table decorated with spiders, bats and ghostly footsteps.

I'm not scared of the dark!

37

Bags of fun

When Ellie and Lottie emptied out their bags they realised they must be good friends because their taste was so similar! Spot what the differences are. See how well you did on page 76.

Illustrations by Stephanie Strickland

41

Cool computer

Boggle your brain and test your skills on these fab computer puzzles.

Circuit

Find the correct path for the electrical charge to flow through the circuit.

Grid reference

Can you find these computer words on the screen?

digital RAM
computer
cable floppy on-line internet monitor program printer
application
scanner
web site
keyboard
mouse mat
software
hard drive

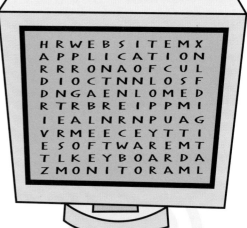

```
H R W E B S I T E M X
A P P L I C A T I O N
R R R O N A O F C U L
D I O C T N N L O S F
D N G A E N L O M E D
R T R B R E I P P M I
I E A L N R N P U A G
V R M E E C E Y T T I
E S O F T W A R E M T
T L K E Y B O A R D A
Z M O N I T O R A M L
```

Screen save

Spot eight differences between these two screens.

Missing Links?

Match the first part of a techno word on the left to its end on the right.

random access
hard
CD
screen
web
on
mouse
www.
floppy

mat
disk
memory
saver
ROM
drive
guides.org.uk
site
line

Scanning

One of these pictures has been scanned into the computer. Work out which one it is.

Look at www.guides.org.uk for the latest on Brownies.

Mouse Mania

There are loads of mice hidden in this picture. Can you spot them?

Wired up

Where is each mouse plugged into the computer?

Illustrations by John Haslam

Are you a computer buff? Find out on page 76.

Extreme south

Antarctica lies at one end of the Earth. In 1911, 90 years ago, a brave Norwegian called Roald Amundsen travelled across it. He was the first person to reach the South Pole.

Ice cold

Most of Antarctica lies beneath a sheet of ice and snow. At the Pole the ice is almost three kilometres thick. The continent has high mountains, glaciers and an active volcano called Mount Erebus. It is also the coldest place on Earth. In August 1990, the world's lowest temperature was recorded there – a massive -88°C! It's cold all year round, and in summer it's still only -28°C.

Roald Amundsen

In 1897, when he was 25, Roald Amundsen joined a team of scientists sailing to Antarctica. It was then that he started planning an expedition to reach the South Pole. Other explorers had the same idea, too, so the race was on.

Antarctica

The South Pole is on the continent of Antarctica, which is a vast frozen land of rock and ice as big as Europe and Australia together.

Expedition facts

Amundsen started for the Pole in October 1911. ✪ He reached it on 14 December. ✪ He raised the Norwegian flag at Polheim, which means 'Pole Home'. ✪ The expedition took 99 days, and he had travelled 3,000 km on foot and sled.

Antarctic animals

There are few land animals, but the sea is rich in plankton which is a mass of tiny floating animals and plants. Plankton is the main food for krill (small shrimps) and fish, which in turn are food for larger animals like seals, penguins and whales.

Whales

In summer, whales visit Antarctica to feed on the krill. The largest is the blue whale. Instead of teeth, a blue whale has a horny substance called baleen. The baleen strains food from the mouthfuls of water the whale takes. A whale breathes through a blowhole on the top of its head, and can hold its breath for over 30 minutes while diving. Its tail is like a huge flipper about seven metres long that it beats to move through the water.

Penguins

Penguins can't fly but are fantastic swimmers. They have waterproof feathers to keep them dry. Under that is a layer of fluffy down and lots of fat which keep the penguin warm. Penguins live together in groups called rookeries.

Freezing life

Antarctica is really a huge cold desert! Despite the cold only about 10 centimetres of snow falls each year. There's very little wildlife, and in winter the surrounding sea freezes covering an area almost as big as Antarctica itself.

Emperor lives

Emperor penguins are the largest penguins and actually live on ice floes in the ocean. The male looks after the egg while the female fishes for food. He keeps the egg warm by balancing it on his feet under a flap of skin. The males huddle together to keep even warmer. Chicks are born without waterproof feathers so rely on their parents to get them food.

Science stations

About 10,000 scientists from 18 countries live and work at bases on Antarctica. The main base is McMurdo Station. It is the most southerly place on Earth that can be reached by ship, though most people travel there by plane.

Chilling facts

About 90 per cent of the Earth's ice is on Antarctica. ❄ The ice stores 70 per cent of all the world's fresh water. ❄ Some places on Antarctica have no snowfall at all making them some of the driest spots on the planet. ❄ About 10,000 tourists visit Antarctica during the summer.

Take a look at the frozen recipes on page 54.

Technostyle

Grab some unwanted CDs and put them to gLittering use with these fab make-it ideas.

Top tip
Cover your work area with old newspaper before you start.

Crazy coasters

You need
pencil ✳ card ✳ scissors ✳ paint and brush ✳ latex glue ✳ CDs

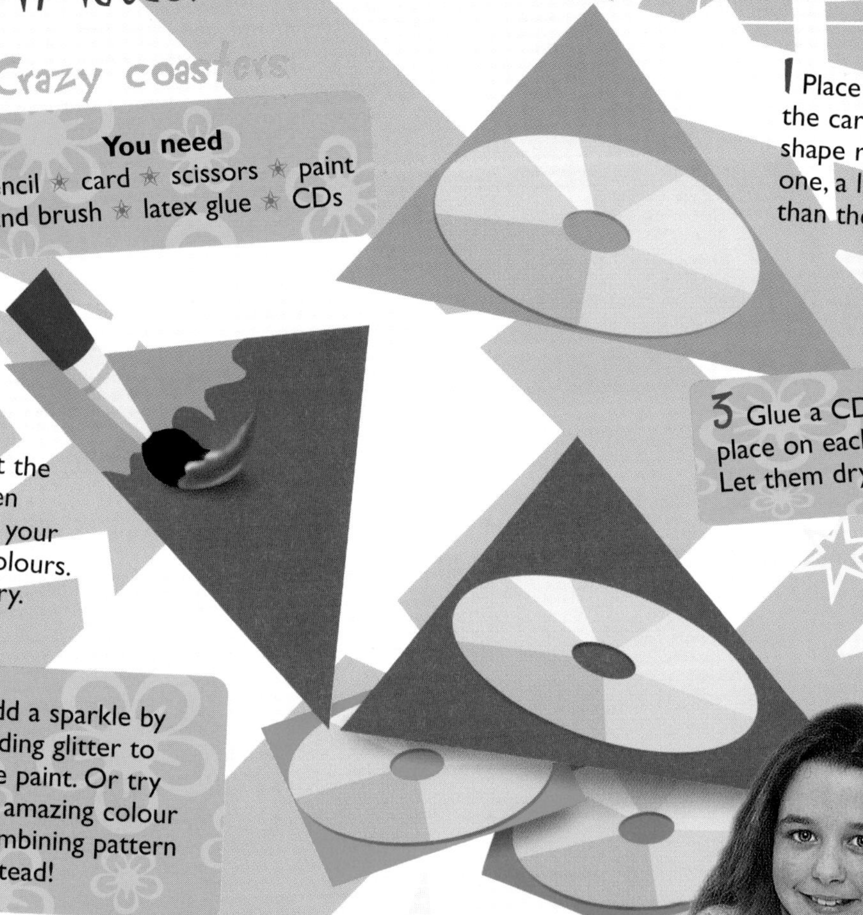

1 Place the CDs on the card. Draw a shape round each one, a little bigger than the CD.

2 Cut out the shapes. Then paint them your favourite colours. Let them dry.

3 Glue a CD in place on each one. Let them dry.

Add a sparkle by adding glitter to the paint. Or try an amazing colour combining pattern instead!

Make sure you use old, spare CDs!

Illustrations by Bill Ledger

46

Monster mobile

You need
old coathanger ✷ paint, pva glue and paintbrush, or glittery sticky tape ✷ plant canes ✷ hacksaw ✷ thin string or tough cotton ✷ 9 CDs

1 Paint the coathanger with a mixture of glue and paint, or cover it with glittery tape.

2 Cut three lengths of string, one about 50cm and the others about 30cm. Dangle the hanger from the back of a chair. Tie the long piece to the hook and the shorter pieces to the ends.

Try a mix of CDs with other glittery bits like Christmas tree baubles.

3 Saw the plant canes into three bits about 30cm long. Tie them to the middle of each bit of string.

4 Cut six more pieces of string of different lengths. Tie one to the end of each stick. Tie a CD to the end of each piece of string. Hang the mobile somewhere bright, inside or out.

Top tip
Ask an adult for help.

Right on time

You need
thick card, 20cm x 55cm ✷ scissors ✷ paint and brush ✷ latex glue ✷ CD ✷ small clock mechanism (available from craft shops) ✷ battery

1 Make folds in the card as shown. In section A cut a hole the size and shape of your clock mechanism.

2 Paint both sides of the card your favourite colour.

C   A   B

3 Glue the CD over the hole. Secure the mechanism in place. Fit the battery and set the time.

4 Fold the card into shape. Glue section B on top of flap C.

No excuse for being late again!

Miss Dorothy

Do you fancy winning one of these fab computers? Read on to find out about an extraordinary Brownie called Miss Dorothy Com and how to enter her great competition.

Adventure girl

Dot's life is packed with adventure and excitement – well, what else would you expect of a Brownie? She's got her own soap opera, so you can follow what she's up to with her faithful dog, Wizard, and Mr Mouse. Read her secret diary to get the latest on what she and her best friend, Genie, are up to at school and Brownies. You'll also get the news of her two mad, mischievous Nans.

Who's Dorothy?

Miss Dorothy Com, or Dot to her friends, has a fab secret. She can jump through her computer screen to travel the Internet. Visit www.missdorothy.com and she'll show you round her cool bedroom, and you can get the latest on her great adventures.

Go on, get surfing at **www.missdorothy.com** and visit amazing Dot.

World life

Dot's also got a brill ITN news service to keep up on what's happening all over the world. There's loads more you can check out with Dot, like e-mail, music and games. So get online and visit her!

Tell Dot your story

Dot loves drawing and writing about her amazing Internet adventures around the world with her friends. What she'd like even more is to get some hot story ideas from you. Dot and Wizard are waiting for your stories and are really looking forward to judging this competition.

Competition

Computer featured may not be final prize.

The prizes

Two great computers are up for grabs – one for the best drawn story, the other for the best written one. The two winners will also see their stories on Dot's web site. There'll also be ten lucky runners-up who get the choice between a copy of Dot Com's First Adventure or a Dot Com mouse mat.

miss dorothy.com
Dot Com's First Adventure!
www.missdorothy.com
by Sharon Doughty with Roger Mills

How to be a winner

All you need to do is draw or write a story about an Internet adventure that Dot gets mixed up in. She may meet a special friend (it could be you!) or have Genie, Mr Mouse or Wizard with her. And don't forget those crazy Nans! Nothing's too amazing for Dot to be involved in!

miss dorothy.com

Miss Dorothy Com is learning about the Internet all the time on her travels and wants to share her knowledge with other children and adults. She's raising awareness of children's issues and is helping charities like The Nelson Mandela Children's Fund and Carol Vorderman's Express Link Up to bring computer and Internet access to children all over the world.

Go on and do it

Draw or write your story.
On the back write:
★ your name.
★ your age.
★ your address.
★ your favourite three things from this Annual.
★ the best thing about being a Brownie.

Put your entry in an envelope and send it to:
Brownie Annual 2001
Miss Dorothy Com Competition
The Guide Association
17–19 Buckingham Palace Road
London SW1W 0PT

Don't forget the stamp. And hurry! The closing date is 31 January 2001.

Read all about it!

Have a go at these fab ways of letting your mates and friends at school know all about the exciting things you get up to at Brownies. You never know they may even want to come along as well!

Poster power

See if there is a bit of space on a noticeboard you can use.

Put a huge heading to attract attention.

Use pictures you've taken when you've been up to something special. Make sure they are clear.

Only put a bit of info on when you meet.

Don't forget a phone number as well. It's got to be your Guider's or another adult's, and you must get the okay from them first.

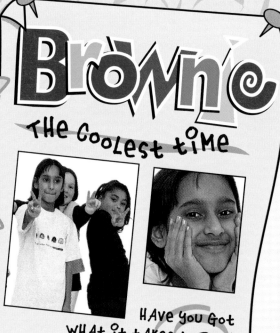

Brownie
THE Coolest time

HAVE YOU GOT WHAT it tAKES to BE A PART of tHE ActioN?

We meet every week during school terms for more information phone Mrs Jones on 0111 223344 or e-Mail: jones@brownies.xxx.com

Reach out

✪ Get one of your pals to join you at a Brownie meeting.
✪ Chat it through with your Guider first so you can plan when will be a good meeting.
✪ Make sure your friend's parents know where she's going. Check with your Guider that it's okay to give out her phone number.
✪ Stick with your friend through the meeting and help her have a good time. Invite her back to your next meeting.

News in hand

As a Six or with all your Pack have a go at making your own four page paper.

Go to a copying shop and ask for some prices. Tell them what size paper, if you want colour copies and how many copies you'll want. Have you got the money? Ask your Guider for some ideas.

How are you going to get it to people? Will your teachers hand some out for you? Can you leave some at the doctor's surgery? What about at your local supermarket? Check your plans with your Guider.

Have you got a computer, or know someone who has? You can always do it by hand.

Dream up a stunning design. Decide on a name and create a masthead across the top.

What's the news? Get your reporter teams out there writing. Don't forget to ask them to get some photos too.

When you've got the stories, decide which one you want to make your leading item. Splash it across the front with a catchy headline.

Don't forget to make up some puzzles as well (put the answers at the bottom, upside down).

Have some info about what you're planning to do in the next few weeks.

Do a news round-up of what each Six is doing.

Give the name of your Guider and her phone number (check it's okay with her first).

Put a couple of other exciting snippets on the front.

Inside do a feature on one exciting Brownie adventure, or something special that a Brownie has done.

On the back feature some more news and photos.

Don't forget your web safety promise at the front of this Annual.

On the web

Why don't you have a go at making your own Pack web site? Ask an adult to help you find out how to go about getting a site up and running. You may need to get some special software and learn how it works.

Use fab pictures.

Click buttons lead you to more information.

Decide what sort of information you are going to put on.

Choose simple words that are really clear.

Brownie info
There's lots of great ideas at www.guides.org.uk or in Brownie magazine every month.

Night in day!

Solar eclipse

A solar eclipse happens when the Moon comes directly between the Earth and the Sun. The Moon blocks the light from the Sun, which makes it go dark on the Earth. The darkness is the Moon's shadow.

An eclipse of the Sun is truly spooky to see. The Sun seems to disappear from the sky, and day turns to night. Find out what'll make it happen on 21 June this year.

Take a Look

On a clear day go out and look at the sky. See if you can spot the Moon. Even though you really notice the Moon at night, you can see it during the day.

Cover up

As the eclipse is about to start the Moon is very close to the Sun. Very slowly it begins to cover the Sun so that it looks like there is a small curve missing from it. Gradually more of the Sun is covered and it starts to get dark as less light reaches the Earth.

Totality

The moment of total darkness is called totality. It only lasts for a minute or two. This is long enough for birds and animals to think that it is night. They settle down to sleep and go quiet. If there are no clouds, stars can be seen. With no sunlight to warm the Earth, the temperature falls.

Background: Oxford Scientific Films/Heikki Nikki. Eclipse, Sequence 1–4: Oxford Scientific Films/Roger Archibald. Eclipse, Sequence 5: Oxford Scientific Films/David Curl. Eclipse, Sequence 6: Oxford Scientific Films/John Mitchell.

Types of eclipse

A total eclipse is when the Moon completely blocks out the Sun. To see a total eclipse you need to be in the exact place covered by the centre of the Moon's shadow. If you are outside the centre of the shadow, then you see a partial eclipse. Not all of the Sun is covered, and some light and heat still reach the Earth.

Did you know?

In ancient times people were frightened of eclipses. They thought the world was coming to an end. The word 'eclipse' comes from an old Greek word which means 'abandonment'. People felt the Sun was leaving, or abandoning, them.

Weird sky

The sky's gone totally odd here. Can you spot which Moon is making the shadow?

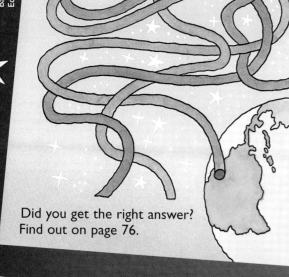

Did you get the right answer? Find out on page 76.

Safe eyes

Never look straight at the Sun. ☆ Never look at the Sun through sunglasses. ☆ Never look at the Sun with binoculars, cameras or telescopes. ☆ Never look at the Sun in a reflective surface, like a mirror or water.

I'm going to get out my special eclipse specs!

See it in the UK

The last time a total solar eclipse was visible from the United Kingdom was on 11 August 1999. The next is on 23 September 2090, but on 31 May 2003 there will be a partial eclipse.

Emerging Sun

As the Moon starts to move away from the Sun, light and warmth return, and the eclipse finishes. It takes about two and a half hours for the Moon to pass completely in front of the Sun.

Round the world

A total eclipse happens somewhere on Earth every year or two. Keep a look out for the next five.

Date	Visible from
21 June 2001	South America, South Atlantic, Southern Africa
4 December 2002	Mid-Atlantic, Southern Africa, South Pacific, Australia
25 November 2003	South Pacific, Antarctica
8 April 2005	Mid-Pacific, Central America
29 March 2006	Central Africa, Western Asia, parts of China

Cool cooks

Have a go at these fab frozen feasts. They are just the thing to cool you down on a sizzling summer day.

Choco-nana

Ingredients
bar of your favourite chocolate ✵ a banana ✵ hundreds and thousands (optional)

You need
saucepan ✵ heat-proof bowl ✵ dessertspoon ✵ oven gloves ✵ lolly stick ✵ cooking foil

Top tips
Ask an adult to help you in the kitchen. ✵ Always wash your hands before cooking. ✵ Tie back long hair.

1 Put about 5cm of water in the bottom of the pan. Start heating the water. Stick the banana on the lollystick and put it in the fridge.

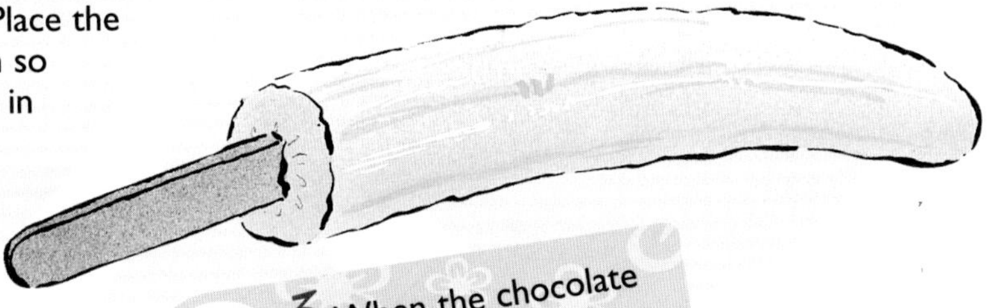

2 Break the chocolate into the bowl. Place the bowl in the pan so the bottom is in the water.

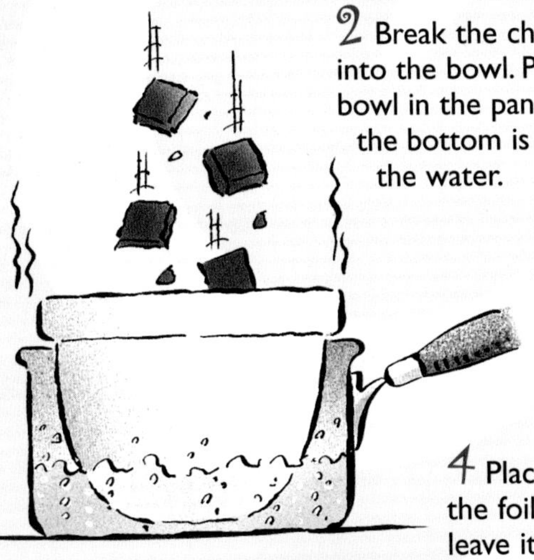

3 When the chocolate melts, smother the banana in it. Spoon the chocolate over it to make sure it is covered.

4 Place it on the foil, then leave it in the freezer for about an hour.

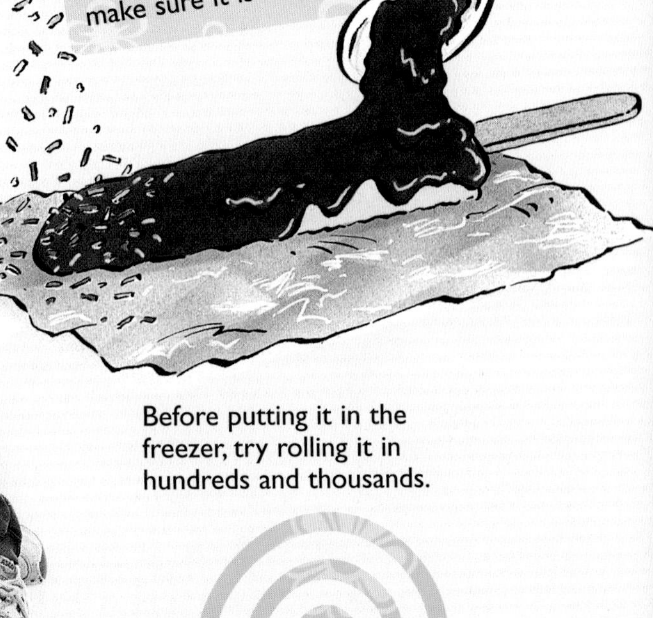

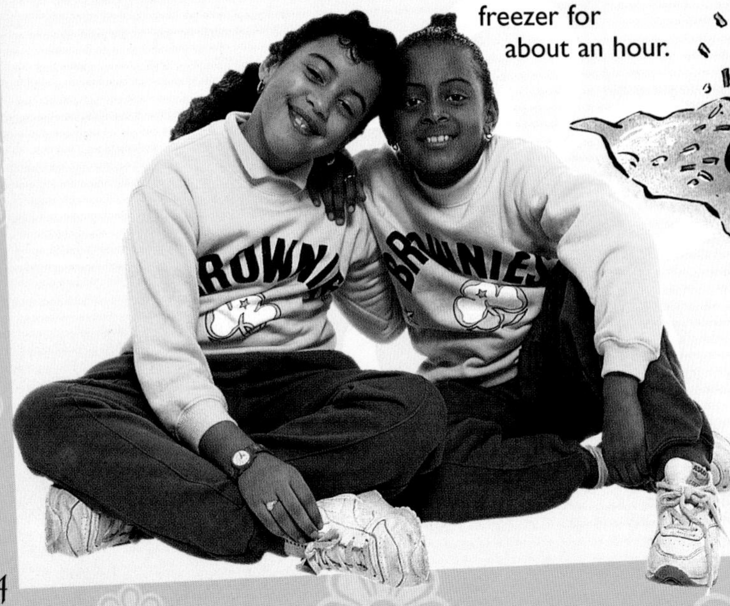

Before putting it in the freezer, try rolling it in hundreds and thousands.

Illustrations by David Pattison and Tom Clayton

Nutty honey-crunch

Ingredients
honey ✹ chopped mixed nuts ✹
vanilla ice-cream

You need
dessertspoon ✹ plate ✹ cooking
foil ✹ teaspoon ✹ ice-cream
scoop ✹ bowl ✹ blender

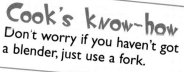

Cook's know-how
Don't worry if you haven't got
a blender, just use a fork.

1 Put two dessertspoons
of honey in a bowl and
leave it in the fridge.

Fruity lolly

Ingredients
fruit juice
or squash (undiluted)

You need
egg cups ❀ little lolly sticks

Fill each egg cup with juice or squash.
Balance them on a tray. Pop them in
the freezer for an hour or two until
they start to freeze. Put the lolly
sticks in place then put them back
into the freezer to set.

2 Put two dessertspoons
of nuts on the foil under
the grill. Toast them lightly.
Let them cool.

Have a go at lots of
exotic fruit flavours like
mango or passion fruit.
Or try making ice-cubes
from fruit squash and
let them fizz in your
lemonade!

3 Mix the nuts and
honey. Put a couple
of scoops of ice-cream
in the bowl.

Freezing point

Spot who's out in the cold.

4 Blend them
together. Pop it
in the freezer
until it resets.

Turn to page 76 for the answer.

55

Jolly, blue giant

The Blue's the biggest kind of Whale
At thirty metres, top to tail.
The largest creature on the earth
(It's seven metres long at birth!)
And as for weight, it's twenty-five
Times any elephant alive.
If you should meet one face to face,
You need not swim away apace
In fear, or even show alarm,
The Blue won't do you any harm.
It isn't that Blue Whales are wimps.
It's just that all they eat is shrimps.

Dick King-Smith

Illustrations by Phil Dobson

Guides are great!

There's heaps you can do to get ready for Guides. So why not start here so you are really clued up? Get ahead of the pack and find out what it's really like.

Where are they?

If you don't know a Guide, ask your Guider for some ideas. She'll know where your nearest Guides meet. Get on the phone and ask for an invite to a meeting.

Name of Guide you know

____

Nearest Guides are

____

Name of their Guider

____

Guide or Guider's phone number

____

Date of meeting going to

____

Starts at ______________

Ends at ______________

Where meeting is

____

____

☐ Tick when you've checked with an adult that it's okay to go.

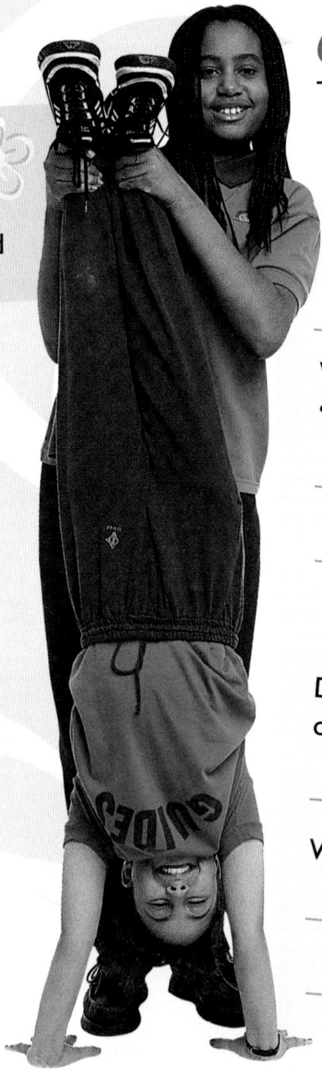

Check it out

There are loads of things Guides do that are like Brownies. Keep an eye out for these.

What do they call Sixes?

____

What are the names of all the 'Sixes' there?

____

____

____

Do they have their own handbook?

____

What's it called?

____

____

Do they wear a Promise badge?

____

What clothes can they wear to Guides?

____

What Guide clothes would you choose to wear?

____

____

Photographs by Diana Anayci and Moose Azim

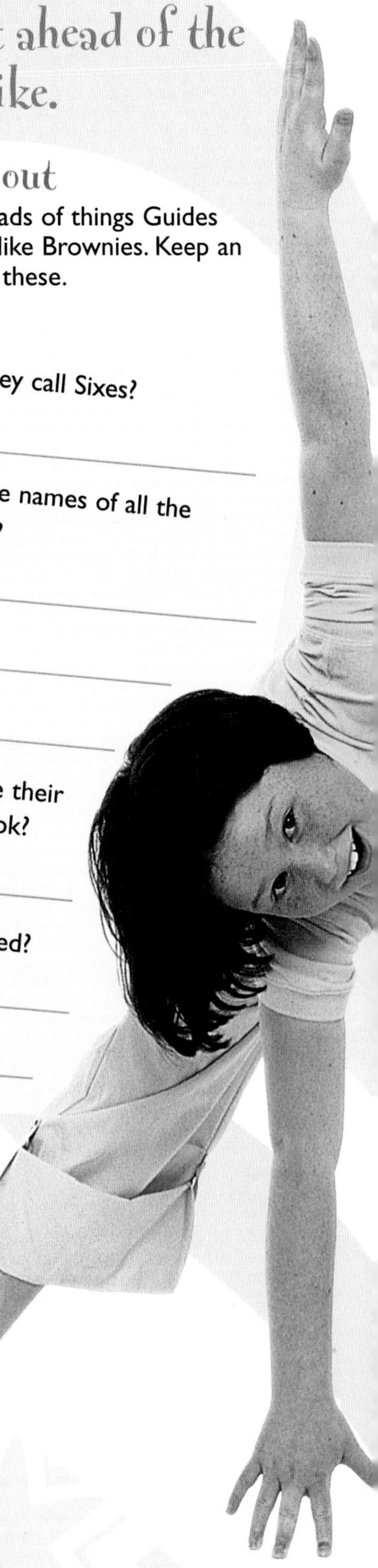

Pick a Patrol

Ask if you can join a Patrol for the meeting. Be ready to have a go at anything. Pick their brains about what they really get up to.

Who's in charge of the Patrol?

_____

Who helps her?

_____

Who decides what they are going to do?

_____

What did you get up to at Guides?

_____

What's the best thing they've ever done?

Where did they go on camp or holiday last?

What's the name of the Patrol?

Write the names and ages of everyone in the Patrol here.

Stick a photo of them here.

Big Guide quiz

Find out if you've got what it takes to be a Guide with this special quiz.

1 I really want to be a Guide because...
a it's better than sitting in front of the telly.
b they go on camp every year.
c I'll have a great bunch of pals called a Patrol.

2 I think the coolest thing about Guides is...
a the clothes they get to wear.
b getting to choose what you do.
c having make-overs and fashion nights.

3 The best Patrol is the one...
a with the oldest Guides.
b that eats chocolate every week.
c that gets out and goes canoeing.

4 I'd like to go to Guide camp 'cos...
a you get to have midnight feasts.
b there are masses of exciting activities to do.
c sleeping in a tent with your mates is magic fun.

5 The funkiest Guide day out would be...
a a day shopping.
b going ten-pin bowling.
c having an adventure day at an outdoor centre.

6 The first thing I'm going to do as a Guide is...
a choose the clothes I'm going to wear.
b suss out the badges I can do.
c start making pals with my new Patrol.

7 If my Patrol had it's own telly channel I'd want to make sure we had programmes on...
a all the fab things we get up to.
b ways to help save the planet.
c exciting things we're planning so others can join in.

8 If I get to be a Patrol Leader, I'm going to make sure...
a everyone gets a say in what we do.
b we have a party every time a new Guide joins us.
c we all have plenty of fun and do lots of stuff.

Going to miss you! Don't forget me.

Tough one? It's easier than you think! Take a look at page 76.

59

Passion for pets

Fancy Life as a vet? Do you know what it's all about? Take a Look at what Jess Gower, chief vet at The Blue Cross Animal Hospital in London, gets up to.

First thing

Even before she leaves for work, Jess is looking after animals. She has a pet cat called Mouse, and two mice, Brown Mouse and Fawn Mouse.

Early duty

Some of Jess's patients have to stay overnight, so at 9.00am Jess checks how they are. At any one time there can be up to 50 patients recovering from operations or illnesses.

Open clinic

Jess works with a team of seven other vets. Twice a day, every morning and afternoon, there's a clinic for sick animals. The vets work out what's wrong with them and what to do about it. Some things they can cure easily with an injection, or a course of tablets or cream. Other things may need longer treatment, or even an operation.

Surgery and dentistry

They have three operating theatres to carry out operations. Jess and the other vets do dental work on animals too, like polishing and descaling teeth.

Vet team

The vets wouldn't be able to do their jobs if it wasn't for the 28 veterinary nurses, two lab technicians, an animal behaviourist, an animal welfare officer, a team of animal ambulance drivers and the reception staff.

Night and day

Throughout the night two people stay to look after the animals. There is also a vet on call to deal with emergencies. During the day there are always lots of patients to keep Jess and the rest of the team busy.

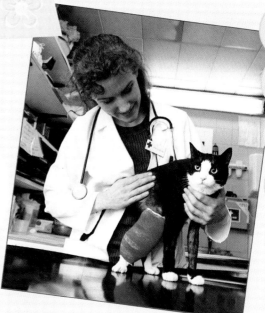

Jess's choice

Jess knew when she was quite young that she wanted to work with animals. She had a pet cat and mouse, but really wanted a pony and a goat. However, she lived in a city so it wasn't possible and instead she spent every weekend helping at local riding stables.

Horses to mice

Jess first wanted to work with horses as a vet. While she was studying at university she had to work with all types of animals, like small pets, farm animals, horses and wildlife. It was then that she decided to specialise in small animals.

Is it for you?

Jess suggests you get in touch with a local vet to find out what it's all about. Some vets look after large animals like farm animals, while others specialise in small pets. Find out what you're interested in by offering to help at a local animal shelter, or see if a local vet will let you go along for a day.

How to be a vet

Apart from being mad about animals, you've got to be ready for a lot of studying. You need good school results to get to university, then it's at least another five years at university.

The Blue Cross

The Blue Cross helps pets whose owners find it hard to afford vet bills. It offers a free service, including pet ambulances, for those who find it hard to get out and about. Take a look at www.bluecross.org.uk for all the info.

THE BLUE CROSS
ANIMAL WELFARE CHARITY

The great

Get stuck in to this great West African game called warri. Once you've made it you can test your wits against a pal. It's not as easy as it seems!

You need

two half-dozen egg boxes or a dozen egg box ❀ scissors ❀ glue ❀ paint and brushes ❀ 96 dried peas, beans, buttons or other counters ❀ nail varnish (optional)

Top tip

Cover your work area with old newspaper before you start.

Trim the egg boxes down, removing the lids, flaps and sticking out parts. Glue the two together. Paint all over and leave to dry. Make two piles of 48 counters. Mark one lot with a dab of nail varnish.

Rules know-how

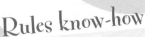

1 Each player divides her pile of counters into two and puts a pile to one side.

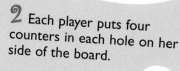

2 Each player puts four counters in each hole on her side of the board.

3 The first player picks all the counters from any hole on her side of the board. Moving to the left, she then drops them one at a time into the next four holes.

4 When she drops the last counter she then picks all the counters from that hole, whether or not they are hers.

5 She then drops all these counters one at a time into the holes round the board.

game!

6 She repeats steps 4 and 5 until a counter is dropped into an empty hole or makes another group of four.

7 If it is dropped into an empty hole her turn ends. If it makes a group of four, then she takes all the counters and puts them to one side.

8 The second player picks four of her counters from a hole on her side of the board. She drops them one by one into the next four holes. She then goes through steps 4 to 7.

9 Keep going until there are no counters left. Each player should have some of her own counters and some of the other player's.

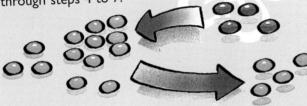

10 Each player separates out the counters she has won from her opponent. She replaces them with counters from her extra pile (step 1). They start playing again by filling each hole on their side with four counters. One player may now have more than 24 counters so she uses a hole on her opponent's side. She may start her turn using these holes. Play again and again until one player has all her opponent's counters.

African adventure

Get yourself round Africa, but take care you do it safely. Can you avoid all the dangers? Take a look at the safe route on page 76.

63

Hair flair!

Short or long? Curly or straight? There's a style out there for you. Try these easy, no-fuss looks and get a new image without getting out the scissors!

Keep it snappy

Comb your hair flat against your head with gel for a wicked wet look!

Get a grip!

Clip in close to your face. Experiment with side and middle partings.

Plaiting easy

Practise this on a friend to get the hang of it, so you can do it behind your own head.

Perfect tail

Gather your hair into a pony tail. Use colourful bungees every ten centimetres.

1 Separate out three bunches about the same length and thickness.

2 Take the right one and pass it into the middle.

3 Take the left one and pass that to the middle.

4 Now back to the right. Keep going to the bottom. Secure with a band.

68

Added twist

Dampen your hair and plait braids all over your head. When they are dry, finger comb your hair gently.

Binder

Separate out a strand of hair. Take a piece of thin wool or embroidery silk. Firmly secure the end, then keep wrapping until it almost runs out.

Carefully twist in another piece as you are wrapping. Keep doing this to the bottom of the strand.

Big clip

Gather your hair into a bunch. Twist it for about 15 centimetres. Flip it up and clip it tight.

Parting moments

From your crown, part your hair at an angle. Or try a zig-zag parting like this one.

Tools to use

Wide-toothed combs are good for combing out tangles, and combing through conditioner.

Turn and clip

Starting in the middle, take a strand and twist it back about two centimetres. Gather a little more hair into the strand and twist again. Keep going till you reach your crown.

Fine-toothed combs are great for creating partings.

Round brushes are great for creating curls.

Mini-clip it in place. Take the next strand down and repeat. Keep going until you reach your ears.

Paddle brushes are perfect for smoothing your hair.

Vented brushes are just the thing when you're using a hair-dryer.

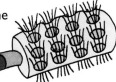

Deep water

At the bottom of the oceans lies a mysterious world, where unusual creatures live in a strange-looking landscape.

Underwater world

It's not easy to get to the bottom of the oceans and seas because they are so deep. Scientists use submersibles like small submarines. The pressure from the water from all sides gets bigger as the submersible goes deeper, so they have extra strong walls.

Oceans and seas

There are five major oceans: the Atlantic, Pacific, Indian, Arctic and Antarctic oceans. Seas aren't as big as oceans and include the North Sea and the Mediterranean Sea. Oceans and seas cover more than two-thirds of the Earth's surface.

Ocean facts

The Pacific Ocean is the biggest. ❀ The Marianas Trench, in the Pacific Ocean, is 11 kilometres deep and is the deepest point on Earth. ❀ The average depth of all oceans is 4 kilometres.

Day life

Shrimps and squid live in deep water during the day, where they are safe from other creatures. At night they swim to the top to feed on plankton, which is the mass of tiny plants and animals that drifts in the sea.

Light in the dark

Some creatures live in darkness all the time, never going to the surface. Some make their own light from chemicals in their bodies. They seem to glow and no one is quite sure why. Perhaps it is to frighten away enemies, or to attract others of their kind, or simply to help them see their food! These creatures are said to be bioluminescent.

Plains and trenches

Most of the seabed is flat and featureless. These huge areas are called abyssal plains and are covered with a thick layer of grey sediment called ooze. In some places there are deep valleys, called trenches which are like huge cracks. They are the deepest points anywhere on Earth.

Fish, fish, fish

Sunlight never reaches the deepest parts of the ocean. At about 900 metres it is totally dark and the water is almost freezing. Plants can't grow here, but many kinds of animals survive.

Seamounts

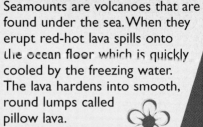

Seamounts are volcanoes that are found under the sea. When they erupt red-hot lava spills onto the ocean floor which is quickly cooled by the freezing water. The lava hardens into smooth, round lumps called pillow lava.

Black smokers

In some places there are towers like 10 metre tall chimneys. These hollow tubes form above holes, or vents, in the Earth's crust. Hot water gushes from them, bringing minerals from deep inside the Earth. The minerals settle and harden onto the towers, making them grow taller. Sulphur turns the gushing water black, so these vents are also known as black smokers.

The flashlight fish has lights under its eyes that act like headlights so it can see its prey.

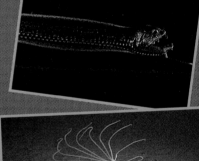

This fangtooth fish is about 12cm long and lives 5,000 metres down in tropical waters eating squids and shrimps.

The deep-water dragon fish has tiny lights along its body. Females grow to about 40 centimetres long but males only reach five centimetres.

This stalked hydroid doesn't have a backbone. Its mouth is surrounded by tentacles that sting its prey. Hydroids can grow to three metres long.

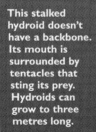

The deep-sea angler fish has a small light in front of its mouth to attract prey. When a small fish comes to look the angler fish swallows it with a sudden gulp.

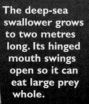

The deep-sea swallower grows to two metres long. Its hinged mouth swings open so it can eat large prey whole.

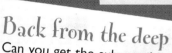

Back from the deep

Can you get the submersible back from the ocean floor?

Did you sink or swim?
Dive into the answers on page 76.

Robots

Some submersibles are robots that are controlled from a ship on the surface. Submersibles are used to make videos and take photographs, and to bring back samples from the seabed.

Submersible, Flashlight Fish, Fangtooth Fish, Deep-sea Angler Fish, Deep-sea Swallower: © Norbert Wu/www.osf.uk.com; Stalked Hydroid: © Ken Smith Laboratory, Scripps Institute of Oceanography/www.osf.uk.com; Dragon Fish: © Peter Parks & Jonathan Watts/www.osf.uk.com. Illustration by David Pattison.

71

Cook-out capers

Have a sizzling time with these make-it-yourself sausages. Serve them up to your mates with a dollop of super special mash. Yummy scrummy at camp or for a cook-out!

Butterbean bangers

Ingredients
500g potatoes ✪ 225g tin butterbeans ✪ 100g cheese ✪ 150g chopped mixed nuts ✪ 3tbsp parsley ✪ oil ✪ 75g white breadcrumbs ✪ 2 eggs ✪ salt and pepper

You need
potato peeler ✪ knife ✪ saucepan ✪ potato masher ✪ grater ✪ mixing bowl ✪ tablespoon ✪ fork ✪ 2 cups ✪ frying pan ✪ fish slice

Top tips
Ask an adult for help. ✿ Always wash your hands before cooking. ✿ Tie back long hair.

1 Peel the potatoes. Cut them into chunks. Boil them for about 10 minutes, until they are cooked. Drain and mash them.

2 Mash the butterbeans in the bowl. Grate the cheese and add it to the beans.

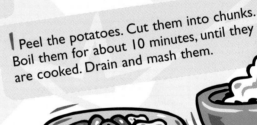

3 Add the mashed potatoes, mixed nuts, parsley, one tablespoon of oil and the breadcrumbs. Mix well with a fork.

4 Separate the egg yolks from the whites carefully using the shells. Beat the yolks. Add and mix into the rest with a little salt and pepper.

5 Make eight balls roughly the same size. Shape each one into a sausage. Carefully fry them, turning them so they get cooked all over.

Try making burgers from the sausage mix, too!

Mouth-watering mash

Ingredients
1kg potatoes ✿ 2 big dessert apples
✿ 30g butter ✿ salt and pepper

You need
potato peeler ✿ knife ✿ saucepan
✿ potato masher

1 Peel the potatoes. Cut them into chunks. Peel the apples. Cut them into quarters. Remove the cores.

2 Boil the potatoes for about eight minutes. Add the apples. Boil for another two minutes until everything is cooked.

3 Drain, then mash with the butter and a little salt and pepper.

Make crunchy mash by adding chopped spring onions instead of apples.

Make it pink by adding a good splash of tomato ketchup as you mash.

Go for gold by boiling chunks of carrots then mashing them in.

On the plate
Serve your sausages and mash with some baked beans and brown sauce.

Odd meal out!

Only two of these meals are the same. Can you spot which ones?

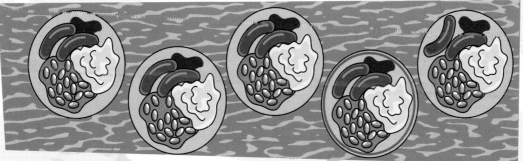

Are you a clever sausage? Take a look on page 76.

Animal antics

These animal puzzles will boggle your mind. Are you ready for the challenge?

Mixed Leads

These dogs have got all tangled up. Work out the owner of each dog.

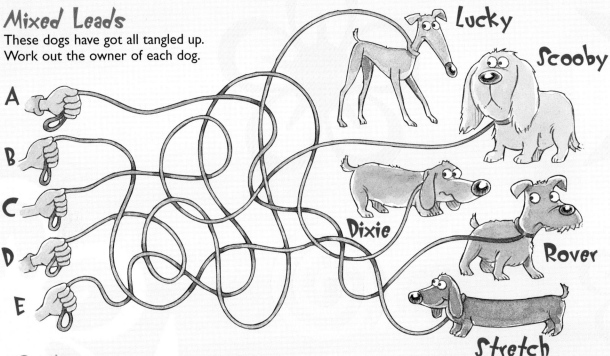

A
B
C
D
E

Lucky
Scooby
Dixie
Rover
Stretch

Spider at home

Work out which two are the same.

A   B   C

D   E   F

American muddle

These North American animals have got all scrambled up. Can you work out what they are?

1 roguca
2 lafbouf
3 bazzylirreg
4 phumnick
5 nukks
6 folw
7 keantalters
8 noraco
9 tilgarlao
10 urbioca

Australian search

Find these animals by linking the letters up, down, backwards or forwards.

- emu
- camel
- possum
- wombat
- echidna
- penguin
- wallaby
- kangaroo
- platypus
- cassowary
- crocodile
- koala bear
- kookaburra
- red back spider
- Tasmanian devil

```
T A I L A B E M A C W
U S V K K U L I L M O
M M E O U R O D E B A
E A D N A R C O R C T
N I A P P Y T A L P
I U G N E U S W R E D
C R Y E A L L A R P I
A A W C B S U E A S K
S S O H Y S M B B A C
A N D I P O O A D E R
K A N G A R O L A O K
```

Food and water

Can you work out how Herbie the hamster can reach his food and water?

Snake ends

Find the beginning and end of every snake.

Illustrations by Tom Clayton

75

Get it right?

See how well you did at the mindboggling puzzles in this great 2001 **Brownie** Annual.

Stripy horse?
(page 11)
Tell them apart

Escape at bedtime
(page 15)
Asteroids

Early morning energy
(page 21)
Breakfast brains

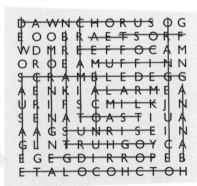

The special message is:
GOOD MORNING

Polar puzzles
(pages 32–33)

Seal feeding

Pick the piece
This piece

Fishing penguin

Polar shadows

Cold links

```
A M W H A L E T N A
L U E U L C R A F R
C N D S B T I O R E
E F E G S C A E E
C L R N U S U B Z Z
L F O Z T H L E R E
O L F E N P O N E S
E A E C I L U S C C
S G W R G N I L O O
S N O E B E C D T T
```

Survival rations

Flake out

New kid on the block
(page 41)
Bags of fun

Cool computer (pages 42–43)

Circuit
The correct path starts with the red button.

Screen save

Missing links

mat
disk
memory
saver
ROM
drive
guides.org.uk
site
line

random access
hard
CD
screen
web
on
mouse
www.
floppy

Scanning

Grid reference

Wired up

Mouse mania

Night in day!
(page 53)
Weird sky

Cook-out capers
(page 73)
Odd meal out!

Cool cooks
(page 55)
Freezing point
It's Freda, of course, on the slopes!

Guides are great! (page 59)
Big Guide quiz
Every answer is the right answer because there are loads of great reasons to be a Guide!

Deep water
(page 71)
Back from the deep

Animal antics
(pages 74–75)

Australian search

Mixed leads
A Rover, B Stretch, C Scooby, D Lucky and E Dixie.

Spider at home
A and E are the same.

American muddle
1 Cougar, 2 Buffalo, 3 Grizzly bear, 4 Chipmunk, 5 Skunk, 6 Wolf, 7 Rattle snake, 8 Racoon, 9 Alligator and 10 Caribou.

Snake ends
• A 5
• B 4
• C 1
• D 3
• E 2

Food and water

All illustrations as acknowledged on appropriate pages

My favourite things

Animal

Group

Sport

Sports personality

Celebrity person

Magazine

Film

Television programme

Computer game

Favourite web site

Colour